Toby: The (Mostly) True Story of a Former Bad Dog

By Stephenie Wilson Peterson

Illustrations By Gozde Eyce

Dedicated to all of the dogs I've known
and loved.

Chapter One

I can explain.

It's all The Cat's fault. Everything was fine until that evil fluffball moved in next door. B.C. (Before Cat), I was a good dog.

I got to ride in the car with my

Human Dad (HuDad). Sometimes, I would even get my own bag of french fries from the drive-through. When HuDad went to work at the restaurant, he would bring treats home for me. I got to take long naps in my doghouse while he worked.

Life was good.

But then that awful cat moved in next door, and my life got all turned around.

It started out innocently enough. The Cat hopped lazily over our fence one day to introduce herself. She swished her bushy tail at me and meowed. Then she invited me to go roam the neighborhood with her.

Leave the yard? I could never do that. Could I? I thought, but The Cat told me it was okay.

She hopped back over the fence, and I followed. Once I landed on the other side and I felt the tingle of freedom on my paws, I knew I'd never be content to stay put in the backyard again.

The Cat ran so fast that I could not keep up with her. She hopped fence after fence. I tried so hard to find her, but her tiny cat paws were too swift for my big, clunky Lab paws. After a while, I was struck with a horrible realization.

I was lost.

I gave up on looking for her and began searching for my house, but along the way I found the most amazing thing I'd ever seen. In the backyard of one of the houses was a cement lake. Later, I heard HuDad call it a swimming pool. It was just sitting there, glistening in the hot sun, begging me to swim in it.

I knew I should head home, but I couldn't resist. That water looked so refreshing. So blue. So swimmable.

Just a few minutes won't hurt, I thought.

So, I got into the lovely water, and I swam and I swam and I swam some more. Isn't swimming the best? I just love swimming!

But then, I realized something. I couldn't get out! I kept swimming, looking for a way to get out, but the pool had a funny ladder that I could not climb. I had no choice but to just keep swimming. I cried and I barked and I howled.

I swam for so long that my legs felt weak. After what felt like hours, a lady came out of the house and saw me in her pool. She helped me get out. I got her all wet. She didn't look happy.

Then, she did something awful. Kids, I am warning you now: this is a bit upsetting.

She waved her finger in front of my face and called me a *bad dog*. I know, it's alarming. But if I'm going to tell you my story, I need to be honest with you.

I'm not a bad dog! I'm a good dog! But that was the beginning of all of it. Everything changed after that moment.

The lady called HuDad, and he came and got me. She yelled at him for a while. We left and then he, too, called me a bad dog. I was crushed. I was sadder than I would be if someone took away all of my chewies. When we got home, I hid in my doghouse and cried for hours.

Chapter Two

The next day,

that evil feline came over to see me again. I told her to stay away from me. I didn't need that kind of negativity in my life. I turned my nose up at her and headed to my doghouse.

The Cat was very persistent. She came over every single day for a month and begged me to go out and play in the neighborhood with her. She made it sound like so much fun. She said there were treats in all of the trash cans.

Finally, I caved. The Cat promised she would not leave me this time. So I followed her over the fence and again was tempted by the freedom of the neighborhood.

But cats, as we all know, are liars.

Soon, The Cat had left me behind. After a while, I was hopelessly lost. But I met another dog!

Hooray for friends, I thought. As I happily trotted up to my new best friend, he snarled.

Then, he leapt forward and bit my paw! I limped away from the mean dog as quickly as I could. This was *not* a friend. He was a foe.

I was so scared!

Cars whizzed past me. Strange smells surrounded me. Loud sounds attacked my sensitive ears. I wandered, hurt and afraid, for what seemed like days. Okay, it might have been an hour. I'm not sure. Dogs are not great with time.

Finally, a familiar smell wafted to my nose. *The Cat.*

If she was near, maybe my house was too! I followed the scent through a field, past a school full of kids, and over a few fences—and then I found my house! I was so happy. I ran up to my door and barked and barked and barked. HuDad opened the door. I was so happy!

Then, it happened again.

"Bad dog, Toby!" he yelled. "Why do you keep running away?"

I wanted to explain it all to him, but I couldn't. I could only whimper. My paw hurt so much. If that icky cat had not tempted me to leave the house, none of this would have happened.

I gave HuDad my best sad eyes and held up my hurt paw. His face softened a bit.

"Are you hurt, Toby?"

I cried again to tell him I was. He leaned down and scratched my ear.

My tail thumped happily on the floor. He pulled the leash off the hook on the wall and clipped it to my collar.

"I better take you to the vet!" HuDad sounded worried.

"Anything but the vet!" I barked, but of course he didn't understand. Why, oh why can't humans learn to speak dog already?

I felt sheer dread as we headed to the car. I stared sadly out the window, looking longingly at my doghouse as we pulled away from the house. Then I saw her.

The Cat. And she was laughing.

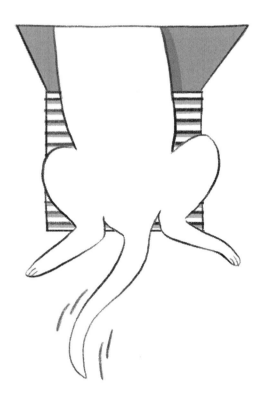

Chapter Three

You probably don't know this,

because you're a human kid, but the vet is the worst place in the world. It's awful. Terrible. Horrible! Don't ever, ever take your dogs there. Why would we want to go to the worst place ever when we are already sick or hurt? Well, we don't, so please stop your parents from doing this to dogs.

Take your cats, though.

Anyway, HuDad took me to the vet because my paw was hurt. The vet looked at my paw and said I needed stitches. Stitches! And they said I had to stay the night just because I ripped out my stitches with my teeth last time. Of course I did! I hate stitches!

I had to SLEEP at the VET!

I was not happy! I mean, would *you* want to sleep there? Think about it. You wouldn't like it. It smells funny, and you have to stay away from your family. It's the worst.

It got late and the vet went home. Six other dogs and I were left in the dark, scary vet's office. In CAGES. They call them kennels, but who are they kidding? We all know that they're really cages. I cried and howled for HuDad, but he couldn't hear me. I sighed and tried to get comfortable.

My cage was across from a window. I stared out the window, looking at the moon and wondering when HuDad would come get me.

Then, I saw something truly horrible.

The Cat. The horrid hairball followed me to the vet! She put her prissy paws up on the windowpane and meowed at me. It's one thing to trick me into leaving the yard, but it's another thing altogether to come to the vet and MOCK me in front of other dogs.

What's coming next is not my finest moment. I want you to remember that my feelings were very hurt and that I really am a good dog. Really.

When I saw The Cat on the windowsill mocking me, I was filled with a rage unlike any I'd ever known before. I needed to break free from my cage! I had to put that cat in her place!

First, I tried to slam myself into

the door to pop it open. I backed up as far as I could and ran at the metal bars as fast as my injured paw would allow.

Bam!

I flew into the door, then my body bounced backward into the cage. The door was strong, but I was sure I was stronger. I ran faster this time, but I just smacked my nose into the cold metal.

I tried a third time and a fourth, but I couldn't get that door to open. The Cat laughed at me mockingly from the window.

I sighed and sat down to try to decide what to do next. My eyes scanned the cage for a weakness I could use to my advantage. I noticed that there was a duct open at the top of the cage. Could I get up there? Where did it go? I needed to know.

I stood on my hind legs and jumped. I missed the opening by a lot. My body flew through the air and fell with a loud thud.

The Cat laughed louder.

Filled with rage and a strength I didn't know I had, I threw myself up the side of the cage and into the hole. Well, most of myself.

My butt dangled out, tail thumping nervously as I tried to figure out what to do. All I could see was darkness. But I didn't let it stop me. I wiggled forward slowly and pulled my butt through the hole. I tried to stand, but the hole was made of metal, and I kept sliding. I started to panic. I was stuck in a scary place!

I slid forward in the hole, away from my cage. I crashed into the side of the tube with a loud thud. Then the whole vent started to sway back and forth. My stomach lurched.

Oh no! I thought. *What do I do now?*

I tried again to run, but I slid and hit the other side. Then, the whole tube fell! I crashed into the ground. It hurt, but I was free. Free to find that evil Cat.

I was still inside. The Cat was still laughing at me from outside the window. I ran to the window and hurled my body into it. The Cat laughed one last time. Then, she flicked her tail and walked away into the moonlit night.

By now, all of the dogs were howling. They could not believe I'd broken out of my cage! They begged me to help them get out of their cages.

From the outside, it wasn't hard to ease the latch open with my nose. I freed them all, starting with a boxer named Max and finishing with a mastiff named Roxy. We all ran wildly around the office. We banged and banged against the front door, desperate to get free.

Suddenly, a loud ringing noise filled the air. We'd set off the burglar alarm! Oops! Soon, the vet came in to try to stop the burglar. The police followed a few minutes later. They searched frantically for the burglar, but they didn't find one. Instead, they found all of us dogs freed from our cages. The vet took one look at the room and the broken duct above my cage, and he knew exactly who set the dogs free.

He pointed his finger at me and said, "Bad dog, Toby."

Chapter Four

My HuDad was very upset

when he picked me up from the vet. I can't see color, but I am pretty sure his face was red. He shook his head back and forth. The whole drive home he muttered to himself. When I tried to lick his face, he pushed me away. *HuDad* pushed me away. I began to think maybe I *was* a bad dog.

When we got home, HuDad looked at me and let out a deep sigh. "Toby, you're too much trouble to be an outside dog. You're going to have to stay inside from now on unless I am with you." And with that, he led me inside instead of out to my doghouse.

At least The Cat can't cause problems if I am in here, I thought.

I thought wrong.

The first few days inside weren't *that* bad. I was bored. And I wanted to run free with the wind in my fur. Being inside has its own perks. There are more crumbs inside. You would be surprised at how much stuff HuDad drops. It's a lot! And when it falls on the floor, he does not mind if I eat it. I got to eat a pancake the first day. That was pretty exciting.

By the third day, the excitement over dropped food wore off a bit. HuDad left for work, and I was stuck inside and alone. I tried crying by the door for an hour, but that did not bring HuDad home, so I sat on the kitchen table to watch for him.

He hated it when I got on the table, but it is right in front of a big window. When I looked out the window while sitting on the table, I could see the whole street. Like a king sitting in his castle looking out over his kingdom, I sat on my table-throne and looked out over my neighborhood and waited for HuDad. I could spot his car from the end of the street so that I could dash to the door to greet him as soon as he walked into the house. That's my job, after all.

I sat on the table and watched a shady-looking child walk to the bus stop. I was just about to bark at him when I heard something from *inside* the house! I sniffed the air, and the fur on my back stood up.

The Cat.

The Cat was inside *my* house! This would not do. Not at all. I tried to quietly hop off the table so I could sneak up on The Cat, but my paw caught a chair on the way down. It fell to the floor with a loud crash, and I rolled as I fell. I landed with my butt in the air and The Cat standing over me, laughing.

I tried to be a good boy. I really did. But she was in my house! And laughing at me! So I did what any respectable dog would do. I chased her. I just wanted to scare her into leaving. But it didn't go that way.

What happened was . . .

Well, try to remember that I'm a nice dog. I just can't stand that Cat. She's as horrible as the sun is hot. And she had invaded my territory. This was an act of war, I tell you!

I lunged at her, barking wildly, spit flying everywhere. She hopped easily onto the kitchen counter, and I crashed into the cabinets. She walked along the counter and used her tiny little cat paws to knock things onto the floor. A coffee cup fell and shattered into a hundred small pieces. Next came the cookie jar. Then, it was the kitchen timer, a whisk, and a cookbook. The kitchen was a mess!

I desperately tried to get up on the counter to get to her, but that only made things worse. As I put my paws up on the smooth countertop, they slid, and I knocked the coffee pot over. Then, The Cat used those tiny, evil paws to open a cabinet. She hopped inside and knocked out glass after glass. She laughed again.

The Cat sprang back onto the counter and spotted a container of flour.

I have to stop her!

I thought as I ran wildly toward her. I

arrived at her side just in time for her to empty the container onto my head.

She laughed and laughed as she jumped down onto the kitchen floor. I chased her as she ran into the living room, but it was too late. She leaped up to the windowsill and sat there for just a moment, looking at me with the evilest grin I'd ever seen. She swished her tail and went out the window, which HuDad had left open a few inches to let fresh air in for me.

I stood in the living room and took in the gigantic mess that lay before me. The kitchen looked like it was hit by a tiny tornado! I'd tracked flour all over the carpet. Shattered bits of glass littered the tile floor. I found pieces of the cookie jar on opposite ends of the room. The seat of a chair lay ten feet from the table.

    This was bad. Very
bad.

Chapter Five

HuDad was so angry

when he got home. I couldn't blame
him. The Cat had wrecked our house.
But HuDad did not know it was that
fuzzy fiend. I took the blame for The
Cat's crimes. Yet again, *I* was called a

bad dog. All I had tried to do was protect our home, but HuDad thought I had wrecked it.

The next day, HuDad left the window open again. I tried to tell him not to. I ran over to the window, stood on my hind legs, cried, and pawed at it.

"Oh, you like the open window, don't you, Toby?" HuDad said.

I whimpered some more to try to tell him the truth, but he didn't understand. He just scratched my ear and headed out the door.

I hopped up on the kitchen table and watched him drive away. I watched an old pickup truck drive by, then a minivan, a man on a bike, and a girl walking her poodle. I stared out at my territory as the warm sun shone down on me. Soon, I was asleep.

I woke up a few hours later to eat my lunch and look for The Cat. That open window worried me. I'd even had a dream that The Cat came into the house and scratched up the sofa. I hopped off the table and went straight into the living room to be sure that she had not damaged the couch while I was asleep. Thankfully, she hadn't.

I sniffed around the open window. The Cat had been there. I sniffed and sniffed to try and figure out how long ago she'd been there. *Maybe it's from yesterday*, I hoped.

But it was not old cat smell. It was new cat smell.

I went to the dining room. HuDad keeps my dish in there so we can eat together. Cat or no cat, I needed my lunch. But the dining room held a horrible sight: The Cat was there, and she was eating *my* food.

I growled and barked and chased that mean cat right out of the house. She slid easily through the partially open window. I wanted to chase after her, but I could only get my snout through the hole.

I was stuck inside with no food. This was very, very bad.

I was starving all day long. Dogs don't do hungry well. I was weak. I was angry.

I was HANGRY!

The next day, I tried so hard to stay awake. I patrolled the house, walking in and out of each room looking for The Cat. Finally, I decided to sit down by the window, which

HuDad had left open yet again. She wouldn't dare to hop through with a big dog like me sitting right underneath the window, would she?

But watching the window got boring quickly. Soon, I curled up in a ball on the floor and took a little nap. I just couldn't help myself. A dog needs at least thirteen hours of sleep a day.

When I woke up, it was too late. The Cat had already come and gone and taken my lunch with her in her belly.

This would not do. I sat on my table and howled. I needed my kibble!

It was DOG FOOD, not cat food!

How dare she betray the sanctity of the supper dish?

This went on for days. I was so hungry, but The Cat was just too sneaky for me. Finally, I had to resort to borrowing some of HuDad's food. I watched carefully each time he opened the fridge so I could figure out how to do it myself. One day, I carefully used my snout to open the door of the chilly food haven.

The first day, I just took some leftovers that were sitting on a plate. He didn't even notice when he got home. What a relief! With my dish constantly empty and the lingering smell of cat that hung over my home, I don't know if I could have taken being called a bad boy again.

For the next few weeks, The Cat came into the house and stole my lunch almost every day. I had no choice but to eat whatever I could find in the fridge. I tried to be a good boy and only take things I did not think HuDad wanted, but it was hard with so many tasty options.

It was around this time that HuDad married HuMom. She moved into the house and gave me a lot of belly rubs and bought me many chewies. I liked her a lot, even if she made HuDad leave me at home when they went out on dates. She's a good girl.

One night, HuDad and HuMom were out on yet another date. The Cat had yet again stolen my lunch, and they didn't come home after work to give me dinner. I was *sooo* hungry.

I headed into the kitchen and nosed open the fridge. There weren't any leftovers sitting on plates for me to snatch. I surveyed the contents of the refrigerator and spotted something heavenly.

A ham.

An entire ham just sitting there, waiting for Toby.

I grabbed it, closed the fridge, and took one delicious bite. Then I heard the car in the driveway. I panicked. If they saw me with this ham, they would call me a bad boy.

I picked it up in my mouth and ran around the house desperately looking for a hiding place. I knew I was running out of time. I found myself in the bedroom and slid it under a pillow on the bed. I'd never seen my humans look under a pillow. I hoped it would still be there the next day for me to eat.

I headed to the door to greet my humans. They scratched my ears and called me a good boy. I was so happy.

My happiness did not last long, however.

About an hour later, HuMom told HuDad that she was tired. She went to the bedroom. I held my breath. Would she find the ham?

Her scream rang through the entire house.

"Bad dog, Toby!"

Chapter Six

The next day,

I waited in the dining room for The

Cat. Of course, I fell asleep again. I woke up to quite the commotion. I heard a crash and a hiss.

I flew into the living room as fast as my feet would take me. The Cat was lying on the ground. She saw me and hissed again. She hopped onto the windowsill and tried to squeeze out the window. Only this time, she couldn't fit.

All of the dog food she'd been eating to spite me had caught up with her, and she'd become quite round. My lunch was one meal too many. Her butt would not fit through the window.

She tried and tried to wiggle her way out, but each time her butt would stick, hanging into the living room.

She was stuck in my house. She pleaded with me not to hurt her.

I wasn't going to hurt her.

I'm a good dog, remember?

I walked away and let her sit on the windowsill as scared as a kid in a haunted house. I rested on my cozy dog bed and stared her down from across the room.

HuDad came home about an hour later. When he walked into the house, I was waiting for him.

"Hi Toby! Did you miss me?" He bent over and scratched my ear. My foot began to thump on my side, and I let out a happy sound. Then, I remembered that it was not time for ear scratches. It was time to get rid of The Cat.

I pushed HuDad toward the living room with my nose.

"Whoa, Toby. What are you doing?"

I pushed him again and whined.

"You want me to go in there?" he asked.

I wagged my tail in agreement and ran toward the living room. HuDad followed. The Cat tried again to squeeze through the window, but it was too late. He saw her, bottom dangling, trying to escape.

"What are you doing in here?" HuDad asked The Cat as he pulled her out of the window. She hissed in return.

"I bet she got in before, and that's what happened in the kitchen," HuDad thought aloud.

I wagged my tail and smiled a

big, happy dog smile.

"Well, I better take you home," he said to The Cat. And he took her next door to the neighbors.

After that day, HuDad closed the window and I got to eat my kibble in peace.

Chapter Seven

With The Cat locked out of the house,

I was able to be a good boy for several days. I told you it was all her fault! As a reward, HuDad started to let me stay outside for an hour or two at a time. Sometimes, The Cat would try to come over and tempt me to leave, but I ignored her completely. I promised myself that I would not let her drag me down again. I was a good boy!

I wish I could say I was able to keep that promise, but I would be lying. She makes it so hard to be good.

After about a month, she hopped over the fence and told me that a meat truck had overturned on the next street. A meat truck! She said the street was filled with meat!

I had to go. I mean, when would I get this chance again? I jumped the fence and headed to the next street. My paws pounded against the street as fast as I could take them in the direction of the tasty, tasty meat. I got there in record time and learned the terrible truth.

There was no meat truck!

The Cat is just so sneaky! And mean! Who would lie about something like that? A *cat*, that's who!

I headed back to my yard, hoping I could get back before HuDad and HuMom realized I was gone. I was sprinting through the neighborhood when a lady pulled her car over right by me.

"Here, doggie!" she called.

I kept running. This was not HuMom. She was someone else's lady, and I didn't have time for her.

"Here, doggie," she called again. "I have cookies!"

Cookies?

Well. My humans could wait a *little* while, couldn't they?

I turned around, tail wagging wildly, and ran toward the woman. She held out a cookie.

"Do you want a snack, doggie?"

I did! I did want a snack. She reached into the back seat of her car and produced another cookie! She gave it to me and grabbed my collar while I munched away.

"Toby: 234 Peach St. Please return me home or call 555-3456 if found."

She scratched my ear and patted the back seat of her car.

"Want another cookie, Toby? Hop in and I will give you a cookie."

I figured she was going to drive

me home. A free ride *and* two cookies? This didn't seem like a bad deal, so I hopped into the car. She closed the door and got into the driver's seat. She tossed another cookie into the back seat and drove away.

But she didn't drive me home. She said if I had a good family, I would not be wandering the streets. She said *she* would take me to her home instead. I did not want to go to her home. My humans are good humans! The best humans! *She* was a bad human, not them!

I howled and barked, but she would not stop. She drove for hours. She drove past rivers and over a mountain. I cried and cried and cried. I did not want to go home with her.

Finally, she pulled up in front of a

small house and dragged me by the collar through the front door.

"Now you have a good home," she told me.

But I already had a good home! I wanted my home back!

I hid under the table for an entire day and night. She tried to get me to come out, but I refused. She tried to give me cookies, but I didn't want her treats. I didn't trust her treats. I ignored her completely. It started to make her mad. She yelled at me for staying under the table, as if being mean would make me like her. I wanted nothing to do with her. She was a bad girl.

Then, I realized it. To fight a *bad girl*, I needed to be a *bad boy*.

I waited until she went to sleep

on my second night there. Then, I came out from under the table and took a look around the house. She had left her closet door open. It was filled with shoes. Lady humans are nuts about shoes. I chewed them all up. Every single pair. I destroyed them all. Then, I pooped in her purse.

But that wasn't enough. I went into the living room, and I peed on the sofa. I chewed up each and every cushion. Feathers flew through the air as I ripped my teeth through lacy throw pillows.

Still not satisfied, I pulled at the carpet with my teeth. When that didn't work, I began to dig at the carpet. I knew there was no dirt under it, of course, but the digging motion was great for tearing things up. It left a huge hole in her carpet.

I looked around the room and took in my handiwork. It was absolutely destroyed, which was exactly what I was going for. I would show her!

Bad human!

Chapter Eight

The bad woman

woke up before I did. I heard her scream, and I laughed to myself a bit.

"Bad dog! Bad, bad dog!" she yelled. "You've destroyed my beautiful home! And my *shoooooes*!"

"Woof," I said, and I wagged my tail. I was pleased to have angered her.

She grabbed me by the collar, marched me out the door, and threw me into the car. Well. That was a little uncalled for.

She hopped into the car and drove. She drove for a long time. Eventually, we passed the mountain and the river. After a long time, she drove onto my street, then right up to my house! I was home!

She walked me up to the door and knocked. HuDad answered!

"Toby!" he called happily. "Thank you for bringing him home!" he said to the bad woman.

"Your dog is a very bad dog. I took him to my home on the other side of the state, and he destroyed it.

He tore up my couch and ate all of my shoes. He also tore up my carpet. I expect you will pay for the damages!"

"Wait. You've had him for days. You had my name, address, and phone number, yet you took him to your house instead of calling me?" HuDad sounded angry.

"A good dog owner would not have let him get out," the woman told HuDad. "So I intended to give him a real home."

"Hey now! He already has a good home.

You stole my dog.

And I am not paying you a cent. He knew he did not belong to you! He was probably just trying to get free to find me."

"You won't get him back unless you pay for the damages," she snarled, one hand on her bony hip and the other clutching my collar tightly.

"If you don't give him back this instant, I am calling the police!" HuDad yelled back.

And with that, she let go of my collar, turned around, walked to her car, and left without saying a word.

My tail wagged a million miles per hour as HuDad knelt down to scratch my ear.

"Good boy, Toby."

Chapter Nine

After that day,

I worked hard to be a very good boy. I didn't chase The Cat no matter how she tempted me. And she tried. Often.

The horrid hairball.

HuDad took me to work at least once a week. HuMom rubbed my belly every single day. I got a lot more rides in the car to go get french fries than I used to. Life was good.

It was like this for several weeks. My humans decided that they trusted me to be outside while they went to work again. They knew I didn't want anything bad to happen. Not after that awful woman took me away, which I have to point out would not have happened if The Cat had not lied about the meat truck. I wish I could tell my humans everything that terrible feline did!

I loved being in the sunshine,

breathing in the fresh air of the yard. It was good to be a good boy again.

Nothing could ever make me leave this yard, I thought to myself as the sun warmed me one afternoon.

The Cat hopped up on the fence and meowed at me. Not her again. I was so sick of that cat.

I explained to her that she wouldn't tempt me into going out of this yard. Never in a million years would I leave this yard. There was nothing I wanted more than to stay here with my humans. I didn't need to leave my home for anything!

But the most horrible thing ever hopped on up onto the fence.

Another cat.

The neighbors got another cat! Who

does that? Isn't one cat enough trouble for a family? But these crazy people now had TWO cats.

Two cats who taunted me.

Every single day.

I tried to be a good boy. But they tortured me.

I didn't know if I could do this much longer. The Cats were so mean.

Maybe if I chased them through the neighborhood just one time, I could scare them away for good. Yes, that was it. I'd just jump that fence and show them who was the boss around here!

Just one more time...

The End

Acknowledgements

I have a wonderful support system. My husband, Nick, and my three kids, Keagan, Eden, and Aviel are my biggest fans. Without their encouragement, this book couldn't have happened.

Throughout my life, I've been lucky to have known and loved many amazing dogs. Their antics inspired this book. Some of those good boys and girls have gone on to the Rainbow Bridge, and I miss them very much. Thank you Willie, Hershey, Ozzie, Murphy, Kirby, Mickey, Boone, Max, Roxy, and of course, Toby for all of the cuddles and joy you brought me. Thank you to Ravenpaw and Leviosa for being by my side every day while I wrote this book.

Thank you to my parents for your unconditional support and for always making sure we had a dog growing up.

Finally, thank you to all of my readers.

About The Author

Stephenie currently lives near Raleigh, North Carolina. Her roots are in the Puget Sound region in Washington State, and she spent many years living outside of Dallas, Texas. She spends her days writing, teaching creative writing, and homeschooling her three kids. Fueled by lots and lots of coffee, Stephenie spends her time hanging out with her family, playing with her rescue dogs Ravenpaw and Leviosa, hiking, and traveling. You can find out more about Stephenie and her work at www.stepheniepeterson.com.

Toby: A Former Bad Dog's (Mostly) True Story of the Great Ball Mystery

Toby's styory continues in *Toby: A Former Bad Dog's (Mostly) True Story of the Great Ball Mystery!* Enjoy a sneak peek of the first chapter.

Available now where books are sold.

Chapter One

I can explain.

It's all The Cats' fault. Those evil furballs are the root of all of my problems. I never got in trouble before they moved in next door.

At first, it was just one cat. And I

know what you're thinking. One cat isn't that bad. Well, you are wrong. One cat *is* bad. She got me in all sorts of trouble. I even got dognapped because of that icky kitty.

Things only got worse when the second one showed up. They teased me all day every day. I didn't know what their fluffing problem was. A dog couldn't even get some peace and quiet in his own yard. It was a shame.

I guess this all started a few weeks ago. It was a perfect day: sunshine, a cloudless sky, and a brand new bone. I was minding my own business because I'm a good dog. I chewed my cool new bone. I rolled in the grass. When a scary-looking baby was pushed by my house in a stroller, I barked extra loud.

You know, good dog
stuff.

While I was barking at the baby,
The Cats jumped over the fence into
my yard. The Original Cat ran over to
my bone and snatched it up! She
carried it away in her evil cat mouth.
The Other Cat ran over to my best
ball, the one with spots, and took it!
The Cats jumped onto the fence with
my things. My feet flew on the grass.
But I couldn't get to them fast
enough. They jumped back into their
yard.

I barked and I barked and I
barked. But I didn't jump over the
fence. Bad things happened when I
did that. I always got in trouble, and I
was trying to be a good dog. All I
could do was bark and whine. My

poor puppy heart broke.

As I watched the sun set, my sadness left me. It changed into something new: rage. I wasn't going to let The Cats take my new bone and my best ball! Even if I was a good dog, I couldn't let bad cats win.

This was war, and I planned to win.

The only problem was I didn't know what to do next. All I knew was that I was going to get back at those cats.

My Human Mom (HuMom) called me from the back door. It was time for dinner and cuddles! My favorite part of the day is when My Human Parents get home! They are the best humans ever.

For some reason, My HuMom had something hidden under her shirt. She had been doing this for a while now. I didn't understand why. As I ran up to her to give her kisses, I nudged her shirt with my nose. Whatever she was hiding felt really solid.

"Down, Toby!" she said. "You have to be careful!"

Whatever she was hiding must have been very valuable. Interesting. Maybe it was cookies!

Cookies are very valuable.

I didn't have time to think about it, because My Human Dad (HuDad) walked in right then. Hooray! I hadn't seen him in forever and ever and ever. I jumped up on him and gave him

3,456 kisses.

"Whoa, Toby! I was only gone for a few hours!" he said.

That silly HuDad can't tell time. He was gone for at least six days. I kissed him some more. My HuDad might not be able to tell time, but it's my job to take care of him. Clearly, he needs my help.

HuDad scratched my ears. My tail thumped and thumped. Happiness is getting ear scratches.

"Where's your new bone?" My HuDad asked.

My bone! Oh, my bone!

I cried and ran to the back door.

"Did you leave it outside?" My HuDad asked.

I cried, trying to explain what happened. My HuDad opened the door. I sprinted outside and barked at the fence.

"The Cats stole it! And my best ball!" I said in Dog language.

Of course, all My HuDad heard was barking. It's really a shame that humans can't learn to speak other languages.

Dogs learn human words, after all.

"Calm down, Toby," My HuDad said. "We'll find your bone."

I know My HuDad loves me because he tried so hard to find it. He looked in my doghouse. He looked in the scratchy bushes. He looked in the flower bed. He even looked under the deck.

He tried so hard, but it was no use. The Cats stole my bone. And my best ball. I was sad all over again. I cried.

"It's okay, Toby. We'll look again tomorrow when the sun comes up," My Dad said.

I heard The Cats laughing from their yard.

Other Books By The Author

Nellie NovaTakes Flight

Nellie Nova's Summer on the Run

Grace's Ghosts

The Day the Librarian Saved the Galaxy

101 Writing Prompts for Kids

Toby: A Former Bad Dog's (Mostly) True Story of
the Great Ball Mystery